TIGER CAN'T SLEEP

by S. J. Fore

illustrated by R. W. Alley

VIKING

To my mother and father, for their lifelong encouragement and support.
And with eternal gratitude to my editor, Janet B. Pascal.—S.J.F.

For Aunt Norma, who has many closets, all equally fun.—R.W.A.

ViKiNG
Published by Penguin Group
Penguin Young Readers Group, 345 Hudson Street, New York, New York 10014, U.S.A.
Penguin Group (Canada), 90 Eglinton Avenue East, Suite 700, Toronto, Ontario, Canada M4P 2Y3
(a division of Pearson Penguin Canada Inc.)
Penguin Books Ltd, 80 Strand, London WC2R 0RL, England
Penguin Ireland, 25 St Stephen's Green, Dublin 2, Ireland (a division of Penguin Books Ltd)
Penguin Group (Australia), 250 Camberwell Road, Camberwell, Victoria 3124, Australia
(a division of Pearson Australia Group Pty Ltd)
Penguin Books India Pvt Ltd, 11 Community Centre, Panchsheel Park, New Delhi – 110 017, India
Penguin Group (NZ), Cnr Airborne and Rosedale Roads, Albany, Auckland 1310, New Zealand
(a division of Pearson New Zealand Ltd)
Penguin Books (South Africa) (Pty) Ltd, 24 Sturdee Avenue, Rosebank, Johannesburg 2196, South Africa

Penguin Books Ltd, Registered Offices: 80 Strand, London WC2R 0RL, England

First published in 2006 by Viking, a division of Penguin Young Readers Group

3 5 7 9 10 8 6 4 2

Text copyright © S. J. Fore, 2006
Illustrations copyright © R. W. Alley, 2006

LIBRARY OF CONGRESS CATALOGING-IN-PUBLICATION DATA
Fore, S. J.
Tiger can't sleep / by S. J. Fore ; illustrations by R. W. Alley.
p. cm.
Summary: A young boy is kept awake by the noisy, "talented" tiger
in his closet that is busy dancing, eating, and making music.
ISBN 0-670-06078-X (hardcover)
[1. Bedtime—Fiction. 2. Tigers—Fiction. 3. Fear of the dark—Fiction.]
I. Title: Tiger cannot sleep. II. Alley, R. W. (Robert W.), ill. III. Title.
PZ7.F75812Tig 2006   [E]—dc22   2005017734
Special Markets ISBN 978-0-670-06249-2 Not for Resale

Manufactured in China
Set in Typeka
Book design by Nancy Brennan

Cozy bed . . . time to sleep.

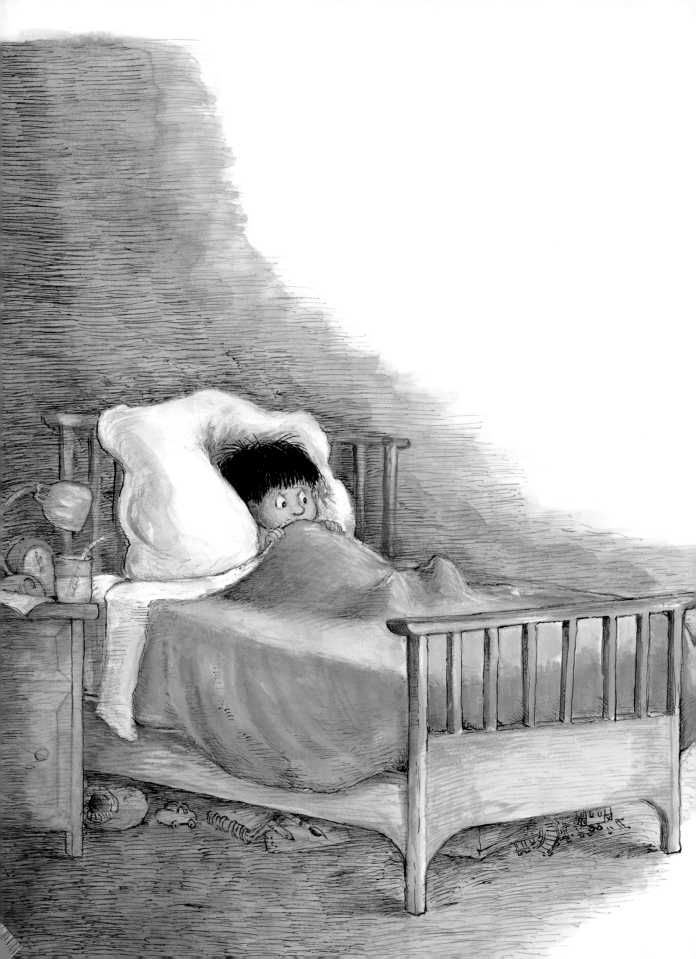

But I **can't** sleep because there's a tiger in my closet . . .

... a tiger in my closet
eating potato chips !

"Shhh! Will you please be quiet in there?
I'm trying to sleep," I tell the tiger.

"Oops! Tiger is sorry. Tiger will be quiet," the tiger says.

Everything is quiet.
I try to sleep.
Then I hear . . .

"Shhh! Didn't you hear me?
I'm trying to sleep!
Will you please be quiet in there?"

"Oops! Tiger is sorry.
Tiger will be quiet now,"
the tiger says.

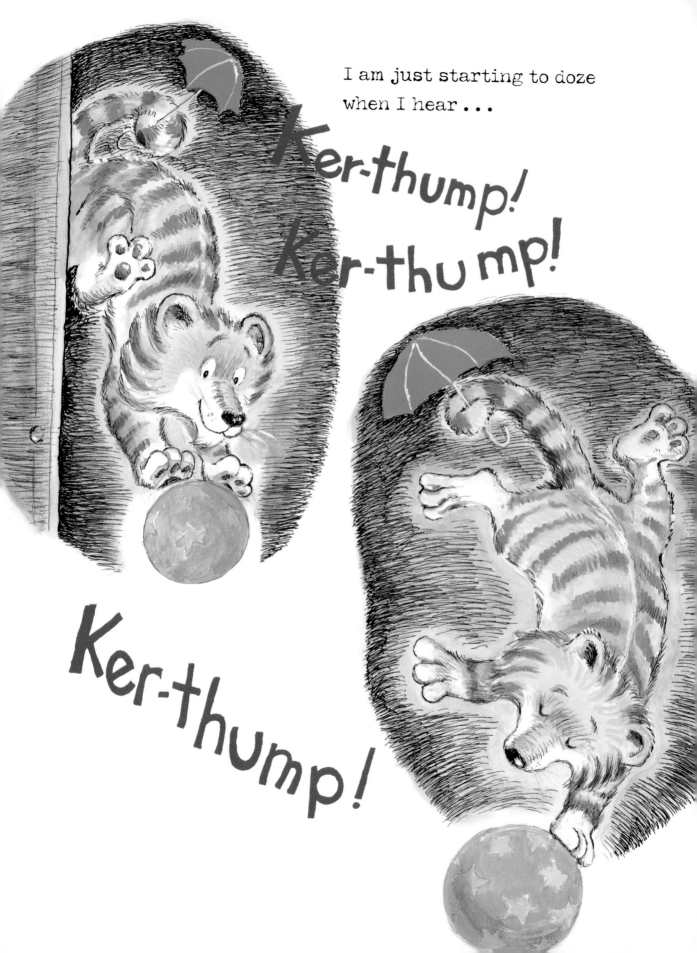

I am just starting to doze
when I hear . . .

Ker-thump!

Ker-thump!

Ker-thump!

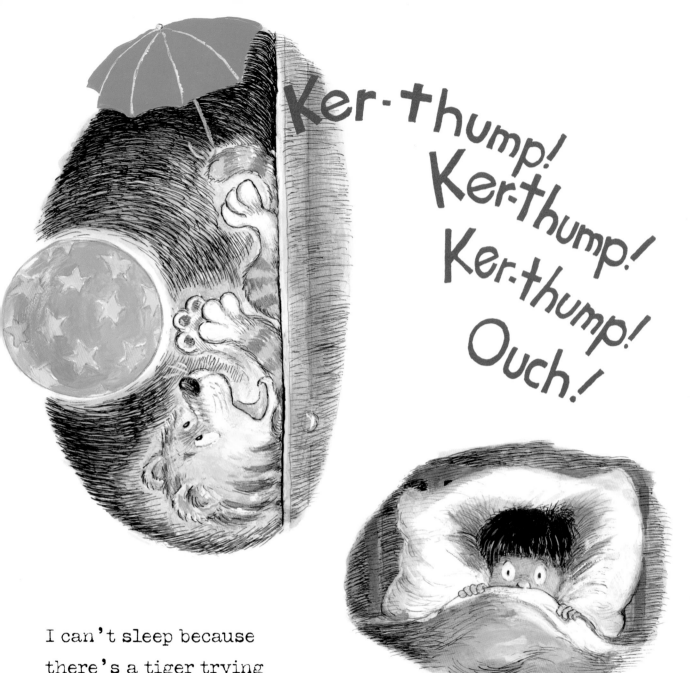

Ker-thump!
Ker-thump!
Ker-thump!
Ouch!

I can't sleep because
there's a tiger trying
to do cartwheels in
my closet and falling down.

My eyes pop open.

"Shhhh!
Please be quiet in there. I can't sleep!"
I tell the tiger.

"And no more cartwheels!
You are going to hurt yourself."

"Oops! Tiger is sorry. Tiger won't make
another sound."

The tiger stops ker-thumping and ouching, and everything is quiet again.

I try to sleep.

But it's impossible to sleep when you have a talented tiger in your closet. . . .

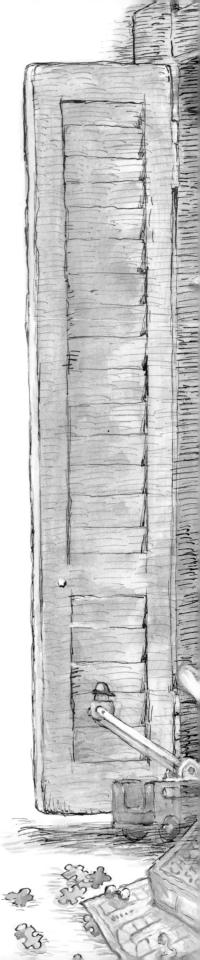

"Shhh, Tiger!

Quiet!

You are driving me crazy!
I'm trying to sleep. I don't want to hear
any more noise.
No tapping. No tuba playing.
No drumming. Not one more single noise!"

"Oops! Tiger is sorry.
Tiger will be very, very quiet,"
the tiger says.

But I don't listen to the tiger
this time.
I take the drum and cymbals
away from him.
I grab the potato chips,
    the ball,
        the tap shoes,
        the banjo,
    and the tuba.

"Now NO MORE NOISE!"

I march back to bed and climb in. Everything is quiet.

Maybe the tiger has finally stopped making noise. I try to sleep. Then I hear . . .

Click-clack!
Click-clack!
Click-clack!

I can't sleep because there's a tiger turning the light on and off in my closet.

"Tiger!

That does it!
STOP! Don't
make me come back
over there!"

"Oops! Tiger is sorry.
Please don't be mad!
Tiger will be quiet
from now on. Promise,"
the tiger says.

The light stops click-
clacking. Everything is
quiet again.

I listen. I listen harder.
I don't hear a thing.
Everything is quiet for one minute.
Everything is quiet for two minutes.
Everything is quiet for three minutes.
I wonder what the tiger is
doing now.
Maybe the tiger is asleep.
Then . . .

"Why are you crying?"
I ask the tiger.

"It's dark in this closet. Tiger is scared," the
tiger says. "Can Tiger sleep in your bed?"

"Um . . . okay," I say.

Tiger hurries out of the closet, runs across my
room, jumps into my bed, gives me a big kiss, closes
his eyes, and pulls the covers over his head.

I close my eyes, too, and listen.
I listen harder. I keep listening. I
don't hear a thing.

I don't hear any crunch-crunch-crunching.

I don't hear any bounce-bounce-bouncing.

I don't hear any ker-thump-thump, ouching.

I don't hear any tap-tap-tap-tapping.

I don't hear any oom-pah, oom-pahing.

I don't hear any boom-boom-boom-crashing.

I don't hear any click-clack, click-clacking.

I don't even hear any boo-hoo-hooing.

Everything is quiet.

Now I'll finally be able to sleep!

Suddenly I hear a noise coming from under
the covers.

It gets louder and louder...
and louder.

I can't sleep
because there's a
tiger snoring in my bed.